The Neverending Tory

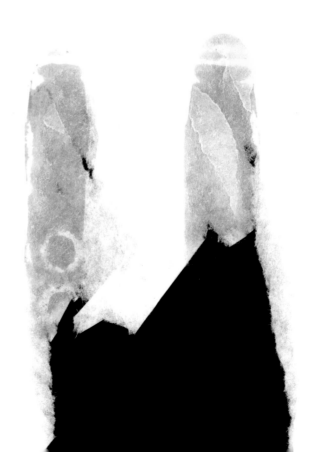

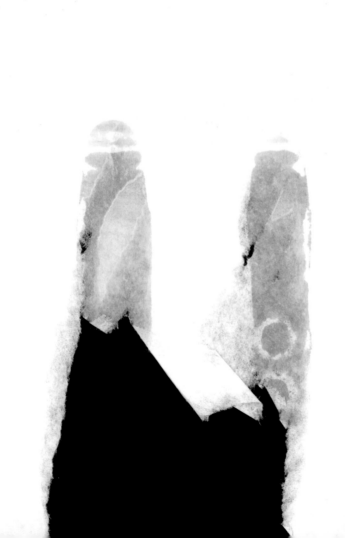

ANDY DONATO

The Neverending Tory
Political Cartoons

KEY PORTER·BOOKS

Canadian Cataloguing in Publication Data
Donato, Andy, 1937–
    The neverending Tory

ISBN 1-55013-469-8

1. Mulroney, Brian, 1939–   –Caricatures and Cartoons.
2. Canada – Politics and government – 1984–   –Caricatures
and cartoons.* 3. Canadian wit and humor, Pictorial.   I. Title.

NC1449.D65A4 1993   971.064'7'092   C93-094119-5

The publisher gratefully acknowledges the assistance of the Canada Council and
the Government of Ontario.

Key Porter Books Limited
70 The Esplanade
Toronto, ON
M5E 1R2

Printed and bound in Canada

93 94 95 96 5 4 3 2 1

Introduction

Well, Peter Worthington has finally run out of nice things to say about me (it took him five introductions). So this time that fateful phone call Peter mentioned in his introduction for *Duds 'n' Scuds* came to me. The voice on the other end wanted me to write the introduction to my latest collection. ME. 'I don't write,' I said, 'I draw.' 'Nonsense,' the voice replied. 'It's only seven hundred and fifty words or so, you can do it.' So here I am with six hundred and eighty-three words to go.

Drawing political cartoons is my passion. I take a particular joy in hearing politicians say things which give their press secretaries migraines, allow the opposition to heap scorn upon them and send the general public into a fury.

The two years since my last collection have been busy ones, filled with politicians tripping all over themselves in an effort to make the front page of the newspapers. I don't imagine many of them ever dreamed they'd end up on the editorial cartoon page instead, often looking just a little ridiculous. It's a good thing for my career that so many of them are so well qualified to be targets of public ridicule. Where would I be without the help of such wonderful people as Joe Clark, and his cross-country constitutional parade; Bob Rae and Floyd Laughrin (especially his budgets); Susan Eng of the Metro Toronto Police Board; Robert Bourassa and the rest of the Quebec gang; and most important of all, Brian Mulroney. As always, Brian has not disappointed in the least: he's had to deal with 13 of his fellow Tories being charged with various offenses; the GST is a neverending (sort of like the Tories) fountain of inspiration; he's had to deal with plummeting approval polls, the constitution and Quebec, Free Trade, Yugoslavia and Somalia, and a tiny little recession.

As 1993 got under way and Brian's approval ratings sank, it seemed as if he was on his last legs, and I began to worry that without Brian life just wouldn't be as funny. After all, political cartoonists pray for people with big chins and a penchant for inserting their feet in their mouths.

Thankfully the Progressive Conservative Party has not let me down. They were kind enough to provide a leadership race rich in material, and I am sure that Prime Minister Campbell and I will have a relationship as wonderful as the one I share with Brian. So far things are going really well—coronations can be fun! Even if Kim isn't elected prime minister in the fall, I still get Jean Chrétien or Audrey Maclaughlin, and no cartoonist could ask for more.

On the slow days in federal politics there was always someone or something to provide me with material. The bungling of various local governments is sure to provide ample fodder, at times surpassing their national and provincial counterparts.

When all was quiet on the home front there was usually something happening in the rest of the world that just called out to be lampooned. There are the attempts of the rest of the world to do something to help the former Yugoslavia; Charles and Di have been good to me for some time now; Mikhail Gorbachev, Boris Yeltsin, the disintegration of the Soviet Union and the efforts of the Western world to introduce them to capitalism; and my favorite and yours—Saddam Hussein—who just can't resist those headlines. Bill Clinton with his saxophone makes a fun target after the proper George and Barbara, and since we seem to be on the way to becoming an impoverished addition to the U.S., this is probably a good thing. I doubt if there will ever be another Dan Quayle, although Kim Campbell seems to be trying, but you can't have everything.

Well, that more or less sums up the last two years from my point of view. I'm sure I haven't covered everything here, but you can be sure this collection hits all the bright (or should I say not-so-bright) spots of the last two years.

I think I'll go play a round of golf—this writing stuff is stressful!

ANDY DONATO

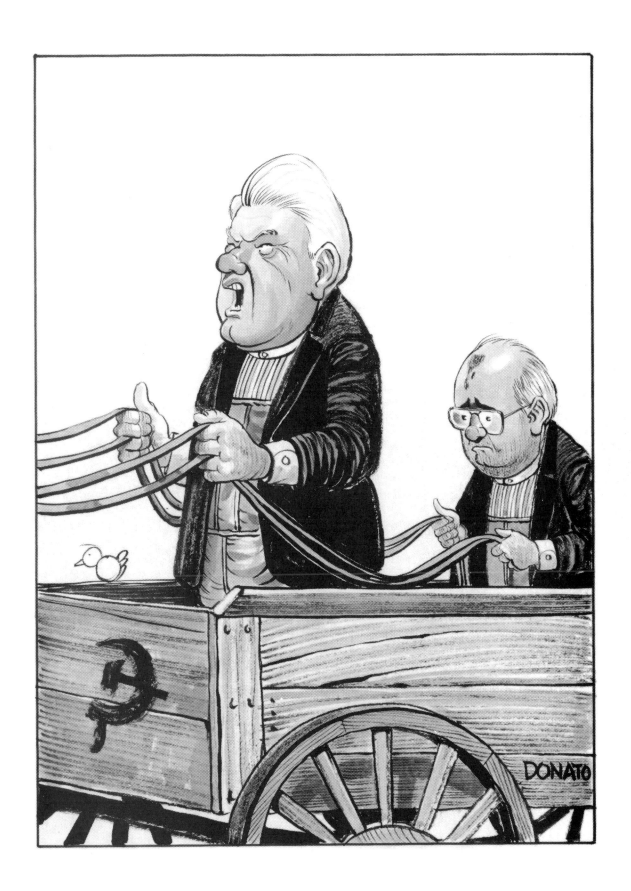

IT WAS 20 YEARS AGO TODAY THE SUN FIRST PUBLISHED IN TORONTO.

I WORKED WITH GREAT EDITORS LIKE PETER WORTHINGTON, BARBARA AMIEL AND JOHN DOWNING!

I WAS GIVEN THE AWESOME TASK OF SAVING DEMOCRACY, BATTLING COMMUNISM AND ATTACKING GOVERNMENT WASTE!

5 CARTOONS A WEEK, 240 CARTOONS A YEAR FOR 20 YEARS...

I FOUGHT THE LIKES OF PIERRE TRUDEAU, DAVID PETERSON AND JOHN SEWELL...

AND WHAT GOOD DID IT DO? WE GOT BRIAN MULRONEY, BOB RAE AND, GOD FORBID, JACK LAYTON!

MOST PEOPLE WOULD SAY I'M A TOTAL FAILURE

IT'S THE ONLY JOB IN THE WORLD WHERE FAILURE CREATES

JOB SECURITY!

DONATO TORONTO SUN

APRIL FOOLS

THE SILENCE OF THE LAMBS

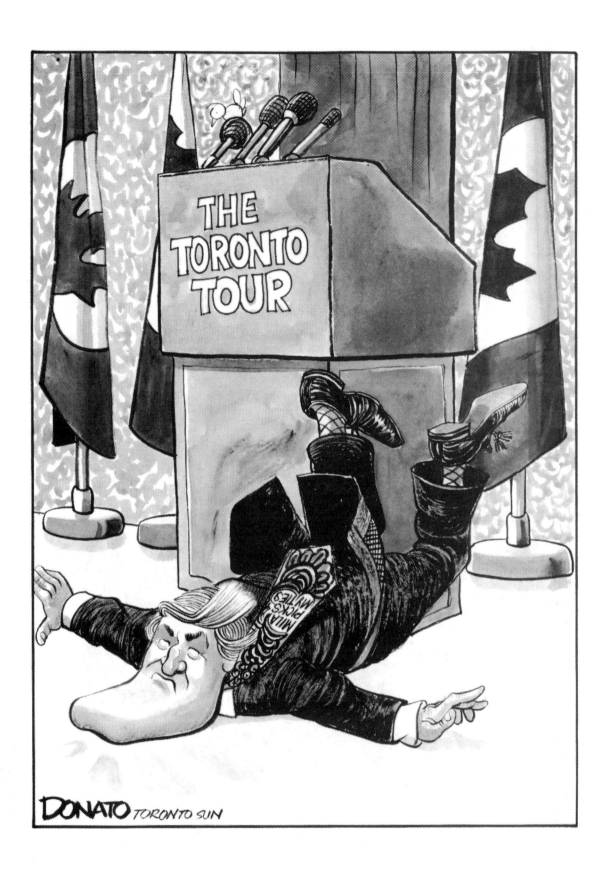

47%

TRANSPORTATION

POLICE

WELFARE

ALL OTHER

RECREATION & CULTURE

AMBULANCE

GENERAL GOVERNMENT

DONATO TORONTO SUN

WIN!!!
A TAX FREE HOLIDAY FOR THE REST OF YOUR LIFE

ENTER THE REFERENDUMB QUESTION CONTEST

RULES
1 ANYONE CAN ENTER.
2 PHRASE YOUR QUESTION IN SUCH A WAY THAT **YES** MEANS **NO** AND **NO** MEANS **YES**.

SEND ENTRIES TO:
REFERENDUMB CONTEST
HOUSE OF COMMONS
OTTAWA ONT.

NAME _____
ADDRESS _____
CITY/TOWN _____
PROVINCE _____
POSTAL CODE _____

? _____
_____
_____
_____
_____

YES | NO

QUAYLE, DANFORTH

DONATO *TORONTO SUN*

TAX FREEDOM DAY

DONATO *TORONTO SUN*

THE
NEW DEAL
MEECH 2
AND THEN SOME

DONATO TORONTO SUN

10 K SUPER BLOWHARD EVENT

STILL GOING!

DONATO TORONTO SUN

CANADA MEXICO U.S.A FREE TRADE AGREEMENT

KAOPECTATE

STILL GOING

UNITY TALKS

DONATO TORONTO SUN

**QUEBEC'S PREMIER MAKING HIS FIRST CALL TO OTTAWA
ON HIS NEW TELEPHONE SYSTEM**

"**I** SUPPOSE IF YOU'RE MR. TRUDEAU
IT'S KIND OF DIFFICULT WHEN YOU GET
UP IN THE MORNING AND LOOK IN THE
MIRROR AND YOU KNOW YOU'VE SEEN
PERFECTION FOR THE LAST TIME ALL DAY. "

BRIAN MULRONEY - SEPT 20, 1992

STILL GOING

UNITY TALKS

DONATO TORONTO SUN

CANADIAN DOLLAR

STILL GOING

UNITY TALKS

DONATO TORONTO SUN

SEPTEMBER 28, 1992

SEPTEMBER 30, 1992

DONATO
TORONTO SUN

STILL GOING

UNITY
TALKS

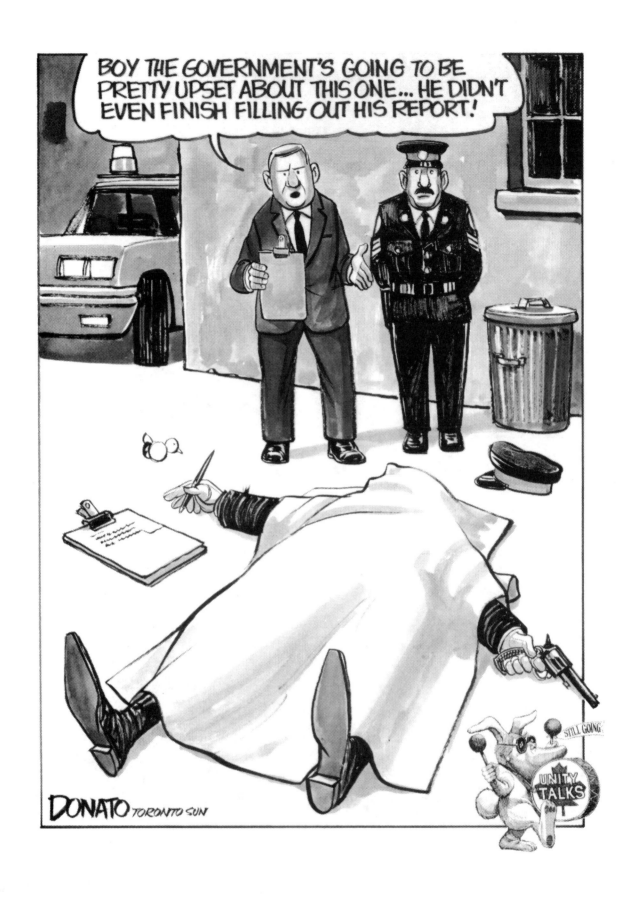

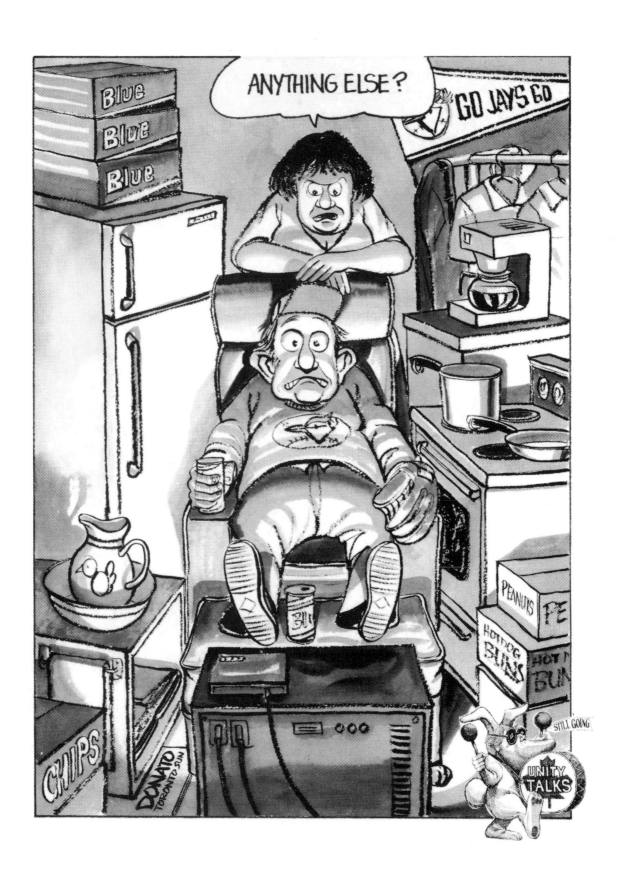

❝GREAT CANADIAN QUOTES❞
FOR TUESDAY OCTOBER 13, 1992

❝IT WILL NOT FALL APART. NO IS NOT GOING TO BRING A CALAMITY THE MORNING OF THE 27TH. THE COUNTRY IS GOING TO CONTINUE...❞

❝ANYONE IN PUBLIC LIFE WHO SAYS TO YOU *'I KNOW WHAT WILL HAPPEN IF YOU VOTE NO'* IS NOTHING BUT A PEDLAR OF ILLUSIONS AND SNAKE OIL❞

STILL GOING

UNITY TALKS

YES!

YES!

DONATO TORONTO SUN

YOU FIGURE IT OUT

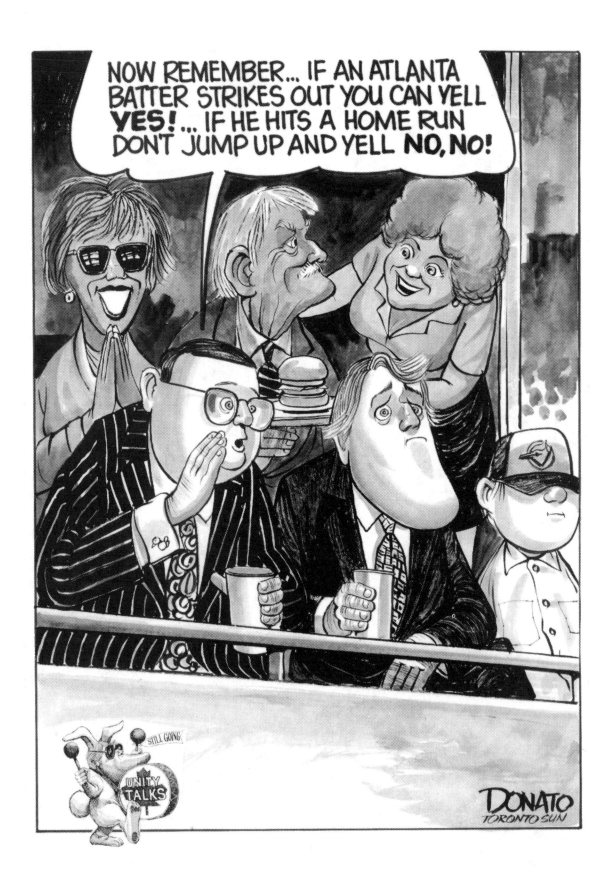

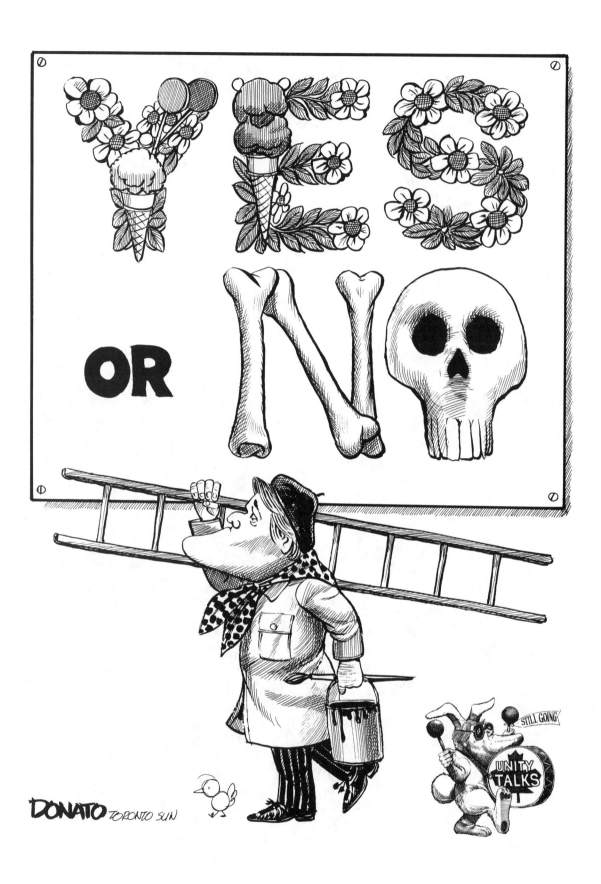

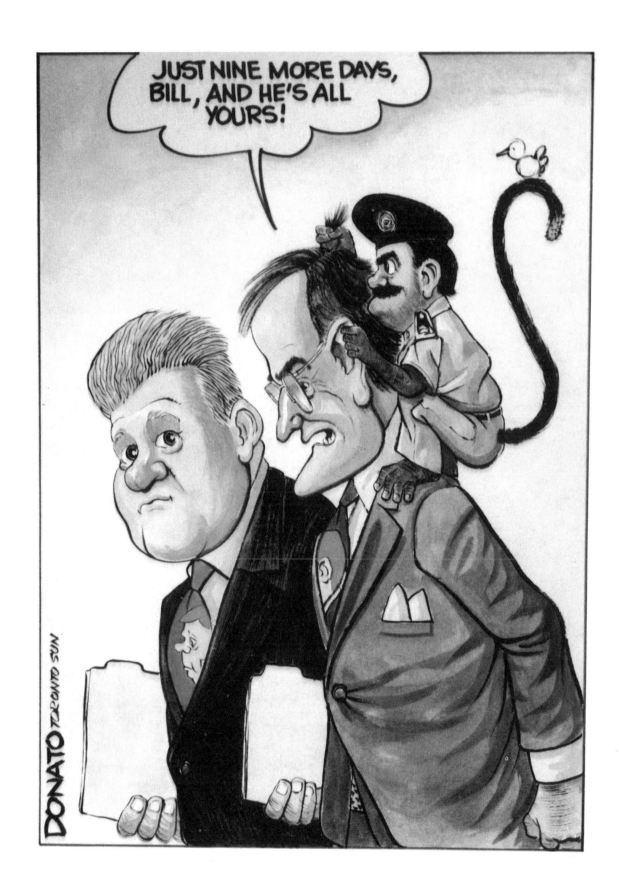

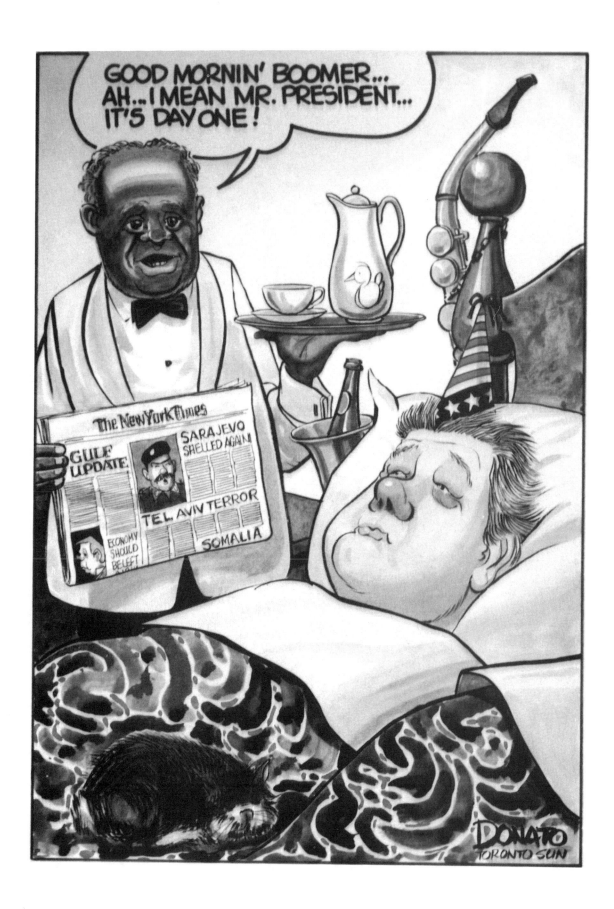

I WANT YOU
FOR THE U.S. ARMY

WE JUST DON'T FEEL THIS IS GOING TO WORK MR. PRESIDENT

DONATO
TORONTO SUN

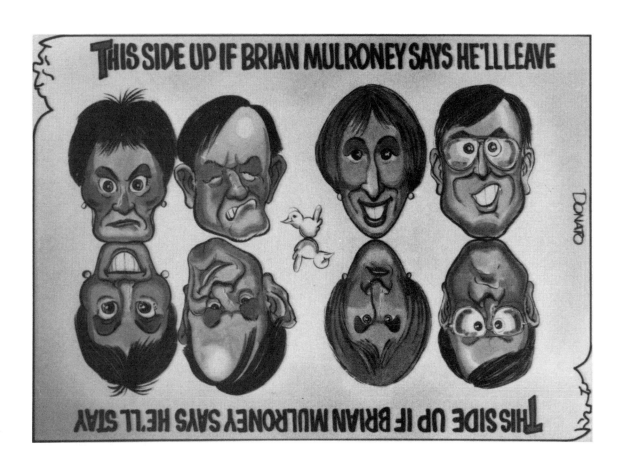

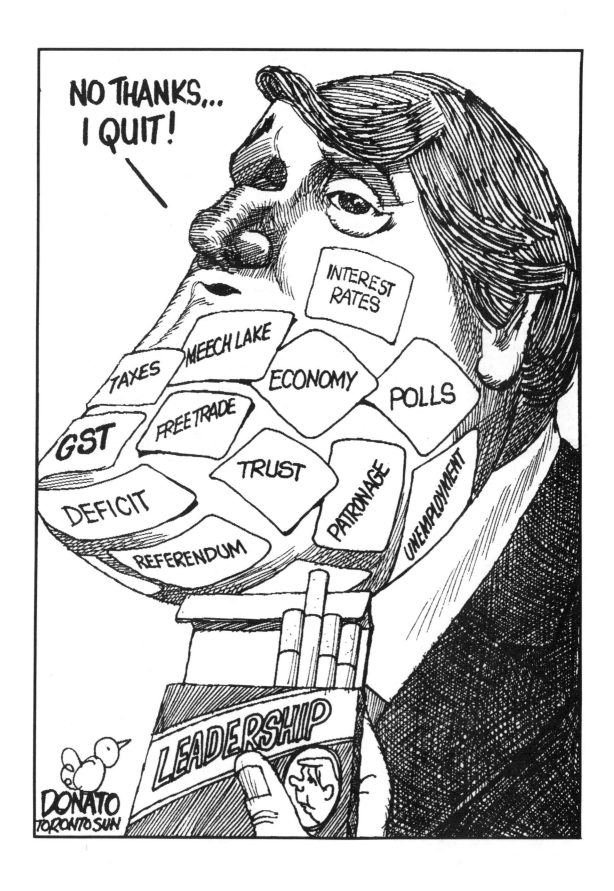

TRIAL BALLOON

ECONOMIC RECOVERY ZONE

DONATO
TORONTO SUN

93-94
BUDGET

ELECTIONS
CANADA

DONATO
TORONTO SUN